| oo | **as in zoo** |

A Making words

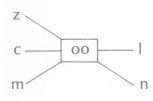   _____ zoo _____
_____
_____

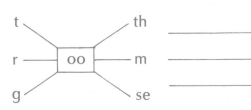   _____
_____
_____

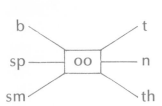   _____
_____
_____

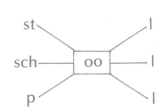   _____
_____
_____

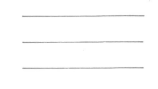

   _____
_____
_____

   _____
_____
_____

B Choose from the seventeen words you have made. Write the correct word under each picture.

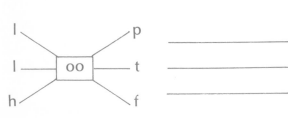   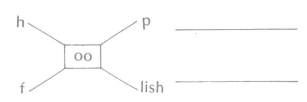      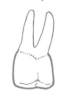

1 _____   2 _____   3 _____   4 _____

C Complete the sentences, using words you have made.

1 A _____ is a small seat without a back or arms.

2 You use a _____ to eat soup.

3 A _____ is a bird like a large duck.

4 A fridge keeps food and drink _____ and fresh.

5 My mum and dad are decorating our living _____.

6 Silk is _____.

D Word pyramid
There are eight words in the squares, all with 'oo' in them. Start at the * to find the words. The last letter of each word is always the first letter of the next word.

1 _____   2 _____
3 _____   4 _____
5 _____   6 _____
7 _____   8 _____

			*s				
		c	h				
	o	o	l	o			
	o	p	o	o	l	o	
o	t	o	o	t	h	o	o
f	o	o	l	i	s	h	o	o	p

1

oo as in book

A Making words

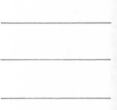

b, t, w, k, k, d → oo → book _____ _____

g, c, r, d, k, k → oo → _____ _____ _____

l, h, s, k, d, t → oo → _____ _____ _____

h, fl, st, k, d, d → oo → _____ _____ _____

B Choose from the twelve words you have made. Write the correct word under each picture.

1 _____   2 _____   3 _____   4 _____

C Complete the sentences, using words you have made.

1 Ann _____ her tortoise and cat to school.

2 If I _____ out of my window I can see the park.

3 Paul's _____ work in art won a prize.

4 When it rains I put up the _____ on my anorak.

D Word meanings

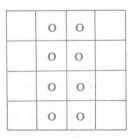

1 black dust after coal or wood has burned | o | o |

2 place where many trees grow | o | o |

3 large black bird with a loud cry | o | o |

4 opposite of bad | o | o |

2

ee | as in sheep

A Making words

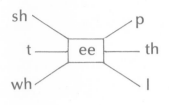
sheep
_____
_____

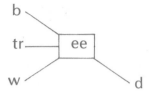
_____
_____
_____

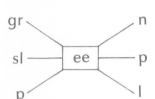
_____
_____
_____

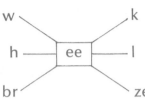
_____
_____
_____

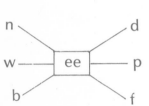
_____
_____
_____

B Choose from the fifteen words you have made. Write the correct word under each picture.

1 _____   2 _____   3 _____   4 _____

C Complete the sentences, using words you have made.

1 There are seven days in one _____.

2 The colour of grass and most leaves is _____.

3 The _____ is the back part of your foot.

4 A _____ makes honey.

D Word meanings

1 wild plant growing where it's not wanted

2 outer skin of a vegetable or fruit

3 time of rest when you aren't awake

4 used for biting and chewing food

5 animal from which we get wool

6 light wind

	e	e		
	e	e		
		e	e	
	e	e		
		e	e	
		e	e	

3

ea as in pea

A Making words

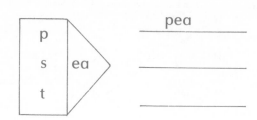

pea
_____
_____

ea + t = _____

ea + st = _____

ea + sy = _____

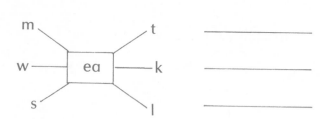

_____
_____
_____

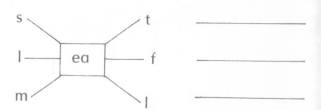

_____
_____
_____

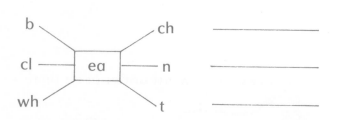

_____
_____
_____

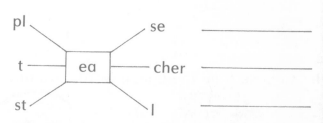

_____
_____
_____

B Choose from the eighteen words you have made. Write the correct word under each picture.

 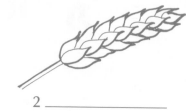  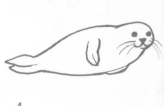

1 _____ 2 _____ 3 _____ 4 _____

C Complete the sentences, using words you have made.

1 The sun rises in the _____.

2 You should _____ your teeth after every meal.

3 We say _____ when we ask for things.

4 Some books are _____ to read and some are hard.

5 The _____ at the seaside is often sandy.

D Word meanings

1 something to sit on

2 to take something that isn't yours

3 someone who helps you to learn things

4 not strong

5 breakfast, lunch, tea, dinner or supper

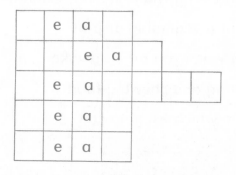

th as in they

A Making words

th + ey = ____they____

th + e = _____

th + eir = _____

th + is = _____

th + at = _____

th + ere = _____

th + ese = _____

th + ose = _____

th + en = _____

th + em = _____

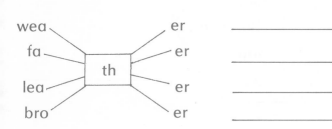

wea / fa / lea / bro + th + er / er / er / er = _____ / _____ / _____ / _____

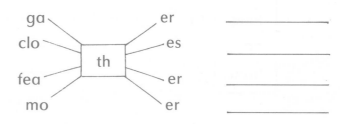

ga / clo / fea / mo + th + er / es / er / er = _____ / _____ / _____ / _____

B Choose from the eighteen words you have made. Write the correct word under each picture.

1 _____   2 _____   3 _____   4 _____

C Complete the sentences, using words you have made.

1 Steven is Janet's _____, and Emma is her sister.

2 My _____ and mother look after my brother and me.

3 If the _____ is warm we play on the beach.

4 My shoes are made from _____.

D Word meanings

1 in that place; not here

2 belonging to them

3 at that time

4 used in speaking about persons, animals or things

t	h			
t	h			
t	h			
t	h			

5

th as in thin

A Making words

in _____thin_____
ick _____
th + ink = _____
ank _____
irty _____

irsty _____
under _____
th + imble = _____
orn _____
eatre _____

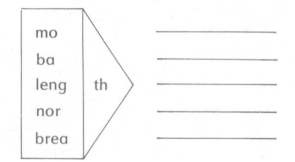

mo	
ba	
leng	th
nor	
brea	

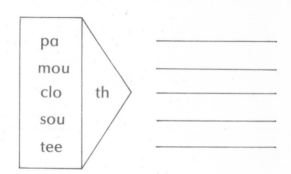

pa	
mou	
clo	th
sou	
tee	

B Choose from the twenty words you have made. Write the correct word under each picture.

1 _____ 2 _____ 3 _____ 4 _____

C Complete the sentences, using words you have made.

1 Kate said _____ you when I gave her a present.

2 Take a deep _____ before you dive into the water.

3 You can see plays acted in a _____.

4 Your tongue is inside your _____.

5 Syrup is a _____ liquid; water is _____.

D Word meanings

1 needing a drink

2 distance from end to end

3 loud noise heard after a flash of lightning

4 to use your mind

5 narrow track for walking along

t	h					
					t	h
t	h					
		t	h			
					t	h

wh as in where

A Making words

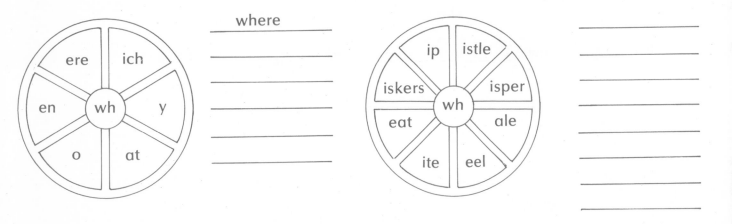

where
_____
_____
_____
_____
_____

_____
_____
_____
_____
_____
_____
_____
_____

B Choose from the fourteen words you have made. Write the correct word under each picture.

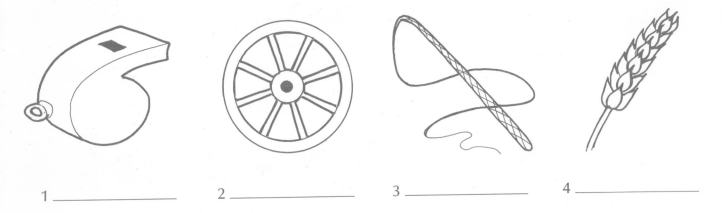

1 _____   2 _____   3 _____   4 _____

C Some of the words you have made sometimes ask a question. Find those words and use them to complete the sentences.

1 _____ time is it?

2 _____ will you be ready to go to the park?

3 _____ is your coat, the grey one or the blue one?

4 _____ is knocking at the door?

5 _____ don't you want to go to school?

D Word meanings

1 to speak quietly

2 ghostly colour

3 very large sea creature

4 found on some animals' faces

5 sound made with the lips

w	h					
w	h					
w	h					
w	h					
w	h					

7

sh→ as in shell

A Making words

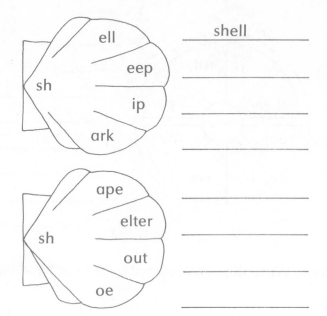

ell — shell
eep — _____
ip — _____
ark — _____

ine — _____
oot — _____
ore — _____
elf — _____

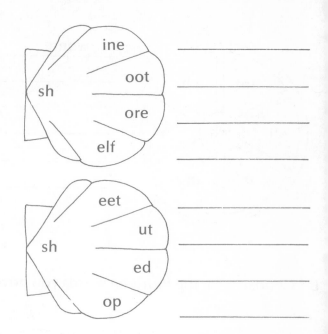

ape — _____
elter — _____
out — _____
oe — _____

eet — _____
ut — _____
ed — _____
op — _____

B Choose from the sixteen words you have made. Write the correct word under each picture.

1 _____ 2 _____ 3 _____ 4 _____

C Complete the sentences, using words you have made.

1 Jane has a blue _____ on her bed.

2 Never _____ under a tree during a thunderstorm.

3 Please _____ the door quietly.

4 A triangle is a _____ with three sides.

5 Brushing your hair every day will make it _____.

D Word meanings

1 small wooden hut

2 to speak in a loud voice

3 worn on the foot

4 large, dangerous fish

s	h		
s	h		
s	h		
s	h		

8

-sh as in fish

A Making words

fish _____

fi •
wi •
hu •
da •
sh _____

ma •
pu •
wa •
di •
sh _____

ra •
bu •
ca •
cru •
sh _____

bru •
fla •
cra •
sma •
sh _____

B Choose from the sixteen words you have made. Write the correct word under each picture.

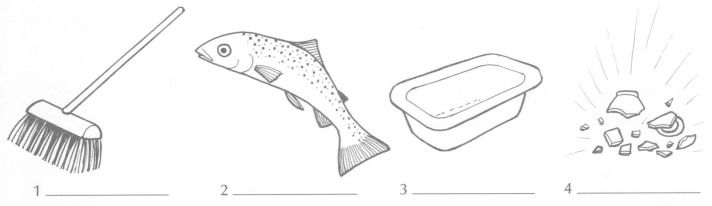

1 _____ 2 _____ 3 _____ 4 _____

C Complete the sentences, using words you have made.

1 We'll have to _____, or we'll miss the train.

2 Don't forget to _____ your neck!

3 Blow out the candles and make a _____.

4 There is a lovely yellow rose _____ in the garden.

5 There was a _____ of lightning, then a _____ of thunder!

D Word meanings

		s	h
		s	h
		s	h
		s	h

1 lots of spots

2 money in your purse

3 opposite of pull

4 Be quiet!

9

ch- as in cheese

A Making words

Add 'ch' to each rung of the ladders.

cheese	___est	___eek	___ocolate
___ild	___ange	___ildren	___oose
___ain	___in	___estnut	___air
___ips	___urch	___ase	___ick

B Choose from the sixteen words you have made. Write the correct word under each picture.

1 _____ 2 _____ 3 _____ 4 _____

C Complete the sentences, using words you have made.

1 There was gold inside the treasure _____.

2 In autumn the leaves _____ colour.

3 There are thirty _____ in Class 8.

4 We collect conkers from a horse-_____ tree.

5 Kiran shared his bar of _____ with Ben.

D Puzzle steps

Do the *Across* clues first.

Across

1 fish and _____

2 made from metal rings

3 to run after someone

Down

1 under your lips

2 food for mice?

3 you can sit on one

10

-ch as in torch

A Making words

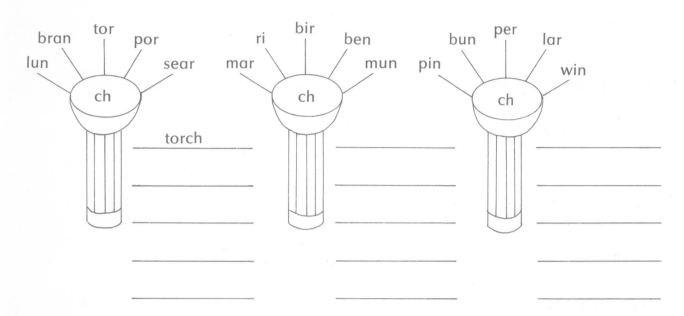

bran, tor, por, lun, sear → **ch**

torch

ri, bir, ben, mar, mun → **ch**

bun, per, lar, pin, win → **ch**

B Choose from the fifteen words you have made. Write the correct word under each picture.

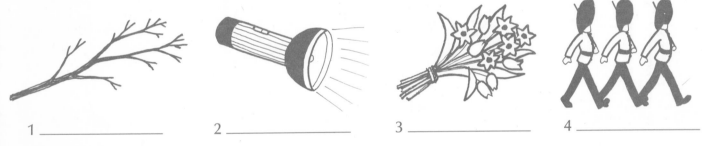

1 _____

2 _____

3 _____

4 _____

C Rhyming words

Find the rhyming words from those you have made.

1 Munch rhymes with _____.

2 March rhymes with _____.

3 Torch rhymes with _____.

4 Winch rhymes with _____.

D Word meanings

Across

2 wooden seat

3 having plenty of money

Down

1 to look for

2 tree with a silvery bark

3 freshwater fish

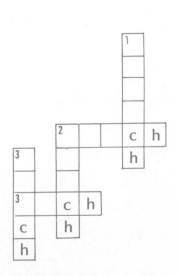

ir as in bird

A Making words

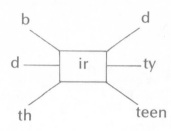

b d
d — ir — ty
th teen

bird
_____
_____

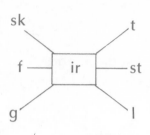

sk t
f — ir — st
g l

_____
_____
_____

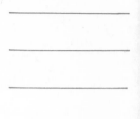

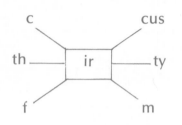

c cus
th — ir — ty
f m

_____
_____
_____

sh t
b — ir — thday
th sty

_____
_____
_____

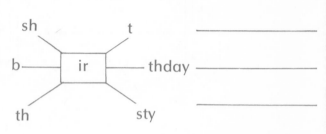

B Choose from the twelve words you have made. Write the correct word under each picture.

1 _____   2 _____   3 _____   4 _____

C Complete the sentences, using words you have made.

1 Pam wore her new red _____.

2 Andrew had seven candles on his _____ cake.

3 David had to climb _____ steps to reach the top of the tower.

4 Emma came _____ in the skipping race.

5 We went to the _____ to see the clowns.

D Word meanings

Across

1 unlucky number?

2 you have one each year

3 creature with wings and a beak

4 number after twenty-nine

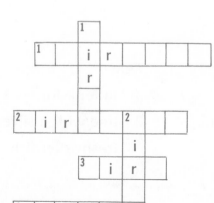

Down

1 opposite of last

2 opposite of clean

12

$\boxed{\text{ur}}$ as in church

A Making words

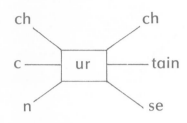

ch — ch — church
c — ur — tain — _____
n — se — _____

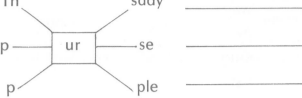

Th — sday — _____
p — ur — se — _____
p — ple — _____

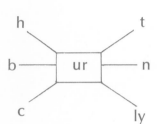

h — t — _____
b — ur — n — _____
c — ly — _____

Sat — day — _____
t — ur — key — _____
b — glar — _____

B Choose from the twelve words you have made. Write the correct word under each picture.

1 _____   2 _____   3 _____   4 _____

C Complete the sentences, using words you have made.

1 A _____ looked after Tom in hospital.

2 We watched the guy _____ on the bonfire.

3 The day before Friday is _____.

4 Pat fell and _____ her arm.

5 On Christmas Day we eat roast _____ and stuffing.

D Word meanings

Across

1 last day of the week

2 thief

3 used to keep money in

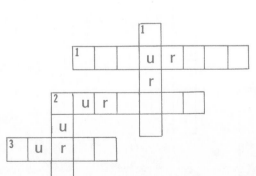

Down

1 opposite of straight

2 to set fire to something

er as in winner

A Making words

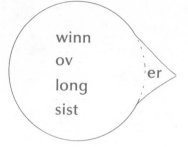

winn
ov
long
sist

er ⟩ winner _____

_____

_____

_____

aft
dinn
fing
fath

er ⟩ _____

_____

_____

_____

moth
wint
und
riv
nev

er ⟩ _____

_____

_____

_____

_____

broth
summ
numb
supp

er ⟩ _____

_____

_____

_____

B Choose from the seventeen words you have made. Write the correct word under each picture.

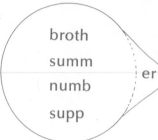

1 _____   2 _____   3 _____   4 _____

C 1 It sometimes snows in _____.

2 Sam's mum said he could go out to play _____ breakfast.

3 The hedgehog curled up _____ the leaves.

4 Peter's _____ has grown a beard.

5 Ceri eats her _____ at seven o'clock, before she goes to bed.

D Word meanings

Across

1 it follows spring

2 opposite of shorter

3 main meal of the day

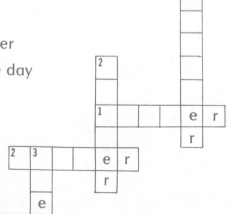

Down

1 sister and _____

2 brother and _____

3 opposite of under

ar as in scarf

A Making words

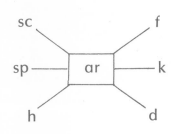

sc   f   scarf

sp — ar — k   _____

h   d   _____

st   t   _____

p — ar — k   _____

f   m   _____

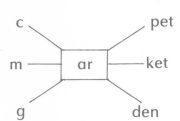

c   pet   _____

m — ar — ket   _____

g   den   _____

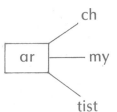

ch   _____

ar — my   _____

tist   _____

B Choose from the twelve words you have made. Write the correct word under each picture.

1 _____   2 _____   3 _____   4 _____

C Complete the sentences, using words you have made.

1 A _____ from the bonfire set the grass on fire.

2 Sita and Kay like playing on the swings in the _____.

3 The _____ is always busy on Saturdays.

4 The new _____ feels soft to walk on.

5 The _____ painted a picture of the boats.

D Help to build the word wall.

1 soldiers belong to this

2 opposite of soft

3 worn round the neck to keep you warm

4 opposite of finish

5 place where cows and sheep are kept

6 found over church windows

a	r			
	a	r		
		a	r	
		a	r	
	a	r		
a	r			

$\boxed{\text{or}}$ as in fork

A Making words

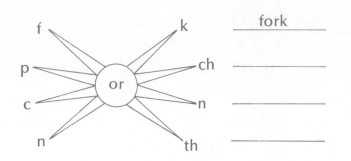
fork _____
_____
_____
_____

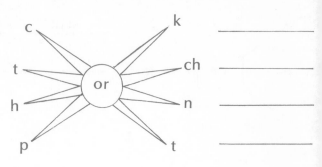
_____
_____
_____
_____

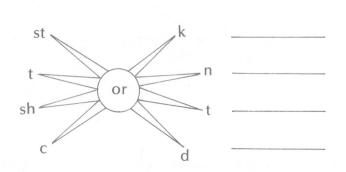
_____
_____
_____
_____

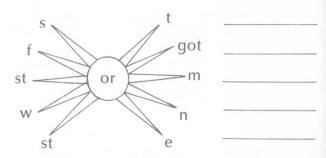
_____
_____
_____
_____

B Choose from the seventeen words you have made. Write the correct word under each picture.

1 _____   2 _____   3 _____   4 _____

C Complete the sentences, using words you have made.

1 Jenny's dress was _____ on a nail.

2 Pam _____ to brush her teeth this morning.

3 Mum thought Emma's dress was too _____.

4 The squirrels are collecting nuts for their winter _____.

5 It thundered loudly during the _____.

D Rhyming words
Draw rings round the words which rhyme with the word in each box.

corn	call	horn	crown	born	worn
port	fort	pant	short	dart	before
cork	car	fork	stork	store	pork
cord	arch	card	ford	snore	lord
torch	catch	scorch	north	porch	touch

16

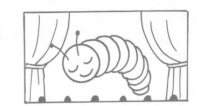

-or as in actor

A Making words

act	actor	
visit	_____	
err	+ or = _____	
collect	_____	
mirr	_____	

mot	_____	
doct	_____	
sail	+ or = _____	
tract	_____	
invent	_____	

B Choose from the ten words you have made. Write the correct word under each picture.

1 _____   2 _____   3 _____   4 _____

C Complete the sentences, using words you have made.

1 The mad _____ nearly blew up his laboratory.

2 This speedboat has a powerful _____.

3 The health _____ came to see our new baby.

4 Ravi is a keen stamp _____.

D Can you crack the code?

a	b	c	d	e	f	g	h	i	j	k	l	m
1	2	3	4	5	6	7	8	9	10	11	12	13

n	o	p	q	r	s	t	u	v	w	x	y	z
14	15	16	17	18	19	20	21	22	23	24	25	26

If a = 1, b = 2, and so on, see if you
can find out what each of these words are.

5, 18, 18, 15, 18 _____   20, 18, 1, 3, 20, 15, 18 _____

1, 3, 20, 15, 18 _____   13, 9, 18, 18, 15, 18 _____

4, 15, 3, 20, 15, 18 _____   19, 1, 9, 12, 15, 18 _____

nd as in hand

A Making words

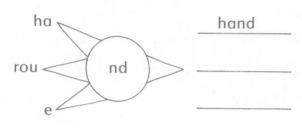
hand _____

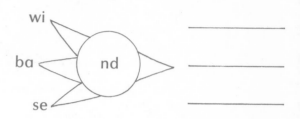
_____

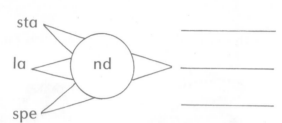
_____
_____
_____

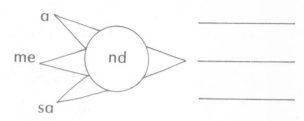
_____
_____
_____

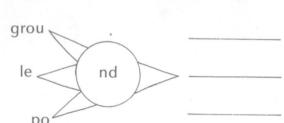
_____
_____
_____

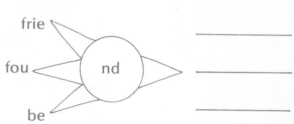
_____
_____
_____

B Choose from the eighteen words you have made. Write the correct word under each picture.

 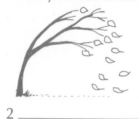 

1 _____   2 _____   3 _____   4 _____

C Complete the sentences, using words you have made.

1 Will you _____ me your book until tomorrow?

2 My _____ sits next to me in school.

3 I like watching aeroplanes coming in to _____ at the airport.

4 The small trees began to _____ in the strong wind.

5 I _____ my pet rabbit hiding in the long grass.

D Word meanings

1 opposite of beginning

2 shaped like a circle or a ball

3 as well as

4 surface of the earth; soil

5 to pay money

			n	d
			n	d
			n	d
			n	d
			n	d

18

ng as in king

A Making words

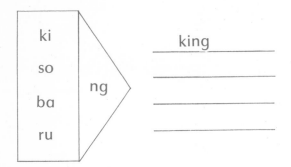

ki		
so		king
ba	ng	_____
ru		_____
		_____

wi		
lo		_____
stri	ng	_____
you		_____
		_____

ri _____

baki _____

spri + ng = _____

divi _____

writi _____

lo _____

si _____

walki + ng = _____

ha _____

starli _____

B Choose from the eighteen words you have made. Write the correct word under each picture.

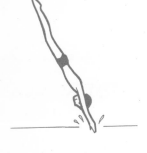  

1 _____ 2 _____ 3 _____ 4 _____

C Complete the sentences, using words you have made.

1 My mother's _____ is made of gold.

2 Daffodils and tulips are _____ flowers.

3 The firework went off with a loud _____.

4 The bird has hurt its _____ and cannot fly.

5 The bus was late and I had to wait a _____ time.

D Word meanings

1 one of the bars or steps on a ladder

2 opposite of old

3 moving about on foot

4 cooking food, such as cakes or bread, in an oven

				n	g
				n	g
				n	g
				n	g

19

nk as in ink

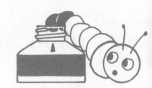

A Making words

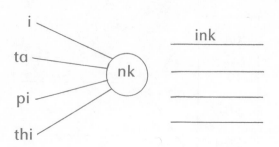

ink

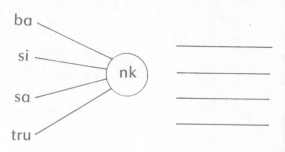

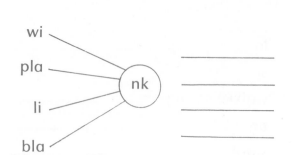

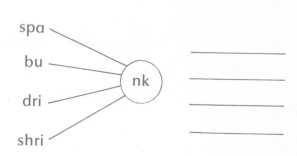

B Choose from the sixteen words you have made. Write the correct word under each picture.

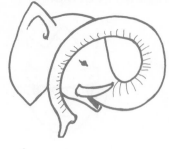

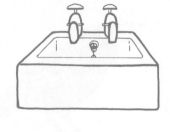

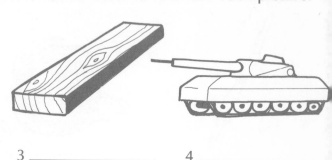

1 _____   2 _____   3 _____   4 _____

C Complete the sentences, using words you have made.

1 After the boat hit the rocks it _____ to the bottom of the sea.

2 I _____ milk every day.

3 People put money in a _____ so that it will be safe.

4 I slept in a _____ in the cabin on board ship.

5 You mix red and white paint to make _____ paint.

D Word meanings

1 coloured liquid used for writing or printing

2 to close and open one eye quickly

3 to get smaller

4 space left empty

5 to use your brain

			n	k
			n	k
			n	k
			n	k
			n	k

20

[nt] as in ant

A Making words

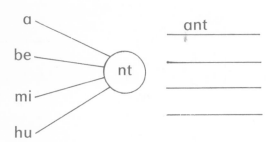

a, be, mi, hu + nt

ant
_____
_____
_____

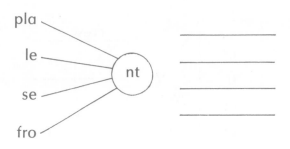

pla, le, se, fro + nt

_____
_____
_____
_____

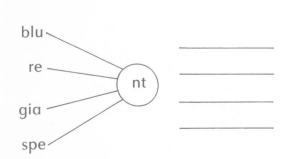

blu, re, gia, spe + nt

_____
_____
_____
_____

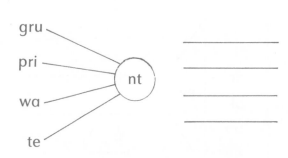

gru, pri, wa, te + nt

_____
_____
_____
_____

B Choose from the sixteen words you have made. Write the correct word under each picture.

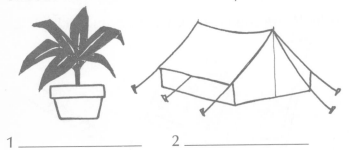 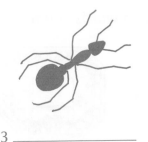 

1 _____   2 _____   3 _____   4 _____

C Complete the sentences, using words you have made.

1 My pencil is too _____ to write with.

2 I _____ my pocket money on a present for my mother.

3 The place where coins are made is called the _____.

4 The lady _____ down to pick up her umbrella.

5 Ann _____ Jennie her bicycle to go for a ride.

D Word meanings

1 rough noise, as made by a pig

2 opposite of back

3 to make letters

4 to wish for

5 money paid to use something which isn't yours

			n	t
			n	t
			n	t
			n	t
			n	t

ew as in crew

A Making words

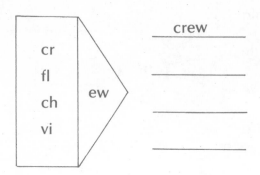

cr
fl
ch
vi
ew

crew
_____
_____
_____

f
d
n
y
ew

_____
_____
_____
_____

st
dr
bl
scr
ew

_____
_____
_____
_____

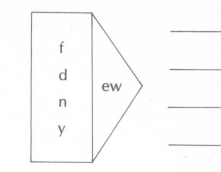

j
neph
n
ew
e
el
spaper

_____
_____
_____
_____

B Choose from the sixteen words you have made. Write the correct word under each picture.

 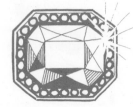  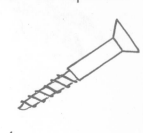

1 _____ 2 _____ 3 _____ 4 _____

C Complete the sentences, using words you have made.

1 Jane _____ a beautiful picture of spring flowers.

2 Only a _____ people came to the concert.

3 We _____ up lots of balloons for the party.

4 The birds _____ away when they saw the cat.

5 You should always _____ your food well before you swallow it.

D Word meanings

1 female sheep

2 evergreen tree

3 people who work on a ship or an aircraft

4 opposite of old

5 son of your brother or sister

		e	w	
			e	w
			e	w
			e	w
			e	w

ea as in he**a**d

A   Making words

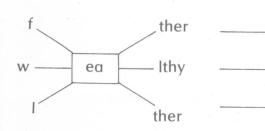

head

_____

_____

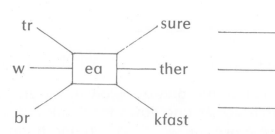

_____

_____

_____

_____

_____

_____

_____

_____

_____

B   Choose from the twelve words you have made. Write the correct word under each picture.

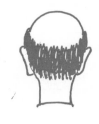

1 _____   2 _____   3 _____   4 _____

C   Complete the sentences, using words you have made.

1   The first meal of the day is _____.

2   Hurry up! Your lunch is _____.

3   The _____ on holiday was rainy and cold.

4   Shoes, gloves and handbags may be made from _____.

D   Word meanings

1   soft and very heavy metal

2   unable to hear

3   having a lot of money

4   hard to lift; of great weight

	e	a		
	e	a		
	e	a			
	e	a		

Check up ee ea

A Word lists

Learn to spell

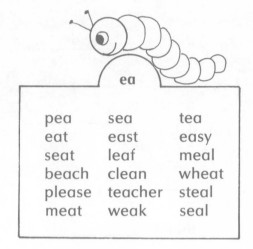

ee		
sheep	teeth	wheel
bee	tree	weed
green	sleep	peel
week	heel	breeze
need	weep	beef

ea		
pea	sea	tea
eat	east	easy
seat	leaf	meal
beach	clean	wheat
please	teacher	steal
meat	weak	seal

B Word search

Hidden in the squares below are twelve of these words which contain either 'ee' or 'ea'.
Search across and down for them and ring them.
Write down the words as you find them. The first one has been done for you.

s	h	e	e	p	a	l	d	s	w	s	g
e	h	t	h	l	s	t	a	i	h	t	r
a	i	h	w	e	e	k	n	h	e	i	e
w	s	m	e	a	t	a	f	g	e	k	e
h	e	l	z	s	l	e	e	p	l	b	n
p	a	q	t	e	a	c	h	e	r	e	t
n	t	g	o	x	b	r	e	e	z	e	w

1 _____sea_____ 2 _____

3 _____ 4 _____

5 _____ 6 _____

7 _____ 8 _____

9 _____ 10 _____

11 _____ 12 _____

C Similar and opposite

Write down words with similar meanings to:

1 cry _____ 2 want _____ 3 dine _____

4 thieve _____

Write down words with opposite meanings to:

5 hard _____ 6 west _____ 7 dirty _____

D What are they?

1 The meat from a bull or cow is called _____.

2 A _____ is a strip of land at the edge of the sea.

3 A _____ is a very large plant with a trunk, branches and leaves.

4 Flour for bread and cakes is made from _____.